INTENTION | I AM | INSPIRED

ISBN: 978-0-9990724-0-0 (hardcover)

ISBN: 978-0-9990724-4-8 (softcover)

Library of Congress Control Number: 2017943995

Printed and bound in USA

2017

Written, edited, and designed by Intention Inspired

intentioninspired.com

30 Days of Brave

—//—

a guided journey

by Intention Inspired

dedicated to the seekers

—*//*—

*to those who step outside their comfort
zone—inspired to make themselves and
the world a happier, healthier place.*

NAVIGATING THE PATH AHEAD

TABLE OF CONTENTS

—⫻—

and the
journey
begins

"Courage is the first of human qualities because it is the quality which guarantees the others."

– ARISTOTLE

Throughout this journey, I can expect to ...

- start each day with a powerful intention
- adopt habits that inspire courageous action
- conquer the internal foe of resistance
- stand my ground and speak my mind
- navigate uncertainty with smarter risks
- thrive with resilience under pressure
- dare boldly to pursue aspirational goals
- overcome self-doubt and move forward
- build a healthier relationship with anxiety
- turn obstacles into opportunities
- rediscover and reclaim lost passions
- gain clarity about the person I aspire to be
- find the courage to be my authentic self

... one inspired intention at a time.

"Tell me, what is it you plan to do with your one wild and precious life?"

—MARY OLIVER

What could you do in 30 days with just a little bit more bravery?

☐ take better care of my body

☐ balance my work life

☐ connect intimately with others

☐ take less for granted and be more grateful

☐ feel what it was like to be a kid again

☐ be true to my most authentic self

☐ chase what I truly desire

☐ _____

Go ahead, be more specific:

_____

_____

_____

_____

My name is _____

and herein lies my brave journey ...

THE INTENTION

WHY A BRAVE JOURNAL?

The purpose of this journal is to serve as a medium for self-knowledge. It has been crafted to inspire brave action toward your most authentic intentions.

All you have to do is chisel out a few minutes each day and let the daily inspiration, guided prompts, and fun challenges awaken your inherently courageous self.

It all started with the question:

"What would best equip ourselves and others to live a braver, more courageous life?"

Bravery comes from within.

It requires an intimate understanding of oneself and the deepest desires that inspire us and leave us truly fulfilled. So by connecting with that pure and true intention, taking courageous action becomes more and more effortless. Eventually, 'brave action' becomes second nature; it's quite incredible!

The ultimate tool for self-knowledge.

Journaling is widely accepted to be an effective practice for the epic endeavor of getting to know oneself more deeply. This guided journal, in particular, has been thoughtfully designed to include key elements of reflection, appreciation, and time with oneself to dig up the weeds and plant healthy seeds for self-improvement.

The truth is, you are already brave!

Just like the muscles and fibers in our body we can train and flex our brave muscle. Over time, in small increments, what seems scary or daunting will eventually become second nature.

It's all about consistent micro acts of bravery.

Everyone can develop and grow their brave muscle. The best way to 'train the brave' is with consistent small acts of courage. As we strengthen our brave muscle, our belief and stamina develop to take on bigger, bolder endeavors.

Time to start training the brave.

This Brave Journal has been designed to help you flex that brave muscle with timeless inspiration, effective exercises, mindful moments, and small wins that form together into one big courageous life. Working hard behind the scenes, each day, is a thoughtfully crafted fusion of inspiration and micro challenges designed to encourage action toward your braver intentions.

Be Brave.
TAKE → Risks.
NOTHING CAN SUBSTITUTE
experience.

BUILDING BRAVERY

HOW TO USE
THIS JOURNAL

———//———

This journal is most useful when used consecutively throughout each of the 30 days. Though you only need a few minutes each day, it is best to do a little preparation and review what is in store for you before we begin.

The power is in the routine.

The most beneficial journaling experience is one that you will do every day. Which is why this journal has been distilled down to its most practical elements.

Five intentional minutes every morning.

That is all that's required to empower your braver self for a successful day. Fitting for a seasoned journaler or a journaling newbie. Whether you leave lines blank or skip entire pages, simply taking a few minutes each day to journal is a micro act of bravery in and of itself.

Define your journaling routine:

The time of day I will dedicate to journaling:

_____

The location I will spend time each day to journal:
(e.g., my breakfast nook, the park, that one cafe)

_____

One other element I will included into this daily routine:
(e.g., background music, a cup of tea, silence my phone)

_____

Choose <u>one</u> 30-day goal.

Have you ever taken on too many projects and goals only to find each doesn't get the attention they deserve? To ensure success and precisely track our progress, this journal was designed to work on a single 30-day goal at a time.

Let's refine and gain clariy on a single 30-day goal to focus on throughout this 30 Days of Brave journey.

A list of my potential 30-day goals:

_____

_____

_____

_____

_____

_____

_____

_____

_____

Questions to consider to choose your goal:

- Which goals are the most realistically achievable in the next 30 days?
- Which one gives me the most satisfaction when I imagine myself accomplishing it?
- Which of these goals, if accomplished, would make others less important or irrelevant?

It might take some thought, or perhaps you knew before you picked up this journal. In any case, spend as much time as you need until you are absolutely excited and convinced to embark on this 30-day brave journey.

My 30 Days of Brave Goal:

_____

_____

_____

Nice work! There will be plenty of opportunity in the days to come to gain further clarity on this goal. So now let's break down how each day will work, so we're prepared to crush it!

1

Calculated

2

Any brave adventure can be broken down into a series of calculated risks. So the more diligent I am in calculating each risky decision, the more prepared I am to prevent the worst from happening. In turn, I have more clarity and confidence to take that next brave step forward.

3

An unknown that makes me hesitant to proceed ...

I'm not sure if I have the time right now to really commit and accomplish my 30-day goal.

One thing I will do today to gain clarity on this ...

Review my calendar to determine what's important, urgent, and unnecessary. I will make the time!

4

[X] Today, I will say 'no' to a pending invitation or opportunity that would deter me from my 30-day goal.

LEFT PAGE ELEMENTS

—*//*—

1   *Today's Intention* is the focus for the day that is fundamental for courageous living. Each has been thoughtfully chosen to progressively develop qualities for a braver life.

2   *An affirmation* is a thoughtfully crafted statement, powerful in helping to embody the daily intention. As you read these words (ideally out loud), assume them as your own. Belief is essential in nurturing that simple intention into powerful change.

3   *Guided questions* are reflections that will awaken braver intentions. Why? Because empty lines can be scary. Because sometimes just a nugget of inspiration will inspire and encourage us to explore somewhere we've never been.

4   *The Daily Challenge* is a fun, immediate way to turn that inspiring spark of intention into a raging fearless fire! Each has been designed to be completed in just a couple of minutes so you can quickly get in a small win and confidently start your day.

RIGHT PAGE ELEMENTS

—*//*—

Along with our guided journal prompts *(on the left of each page)*, there is tremendous value in creating space for life's unexpected moments, extrapolating ideas, and reflecting on what the day brought *(on the right side of each page)*.

5   *A quote* from history's bravest and wisest to stimulate positive free-flowing thoughts.

6   *Daily Moment of Gratitude* because gratefulness is the antidote to fear. Which deserves it's own page to explain, found on the following page (24).

7   *Morning inspiration* is yours to do with as you're inspired. Perhaps you'd like to expound further on the intention of the day, explore any insights, draw a doodle, or simply express what's on your mind.

8   *Evening reflection* is a collection of the highs and lows that the day brought. Who inspired me today? How was I challenged? What would I have done differently today? What memories are worth saving?

5 *"Logic will get you from A to B. Imagination will take you everywhere."*
— ALBERT EINSTEIN

6 I am grateful for ...

my beating heart

a perfectly ripe avocado

friends and family who support me

7 Morning inspiration ...

Soaking up the crisp morning air. Everything is still
sleeping. Yet another fresh start. A reminder that
everything that's been created all started with a
thought. Today, I will think big and act boldly.

8 Evening reflection ...

I made an extra batch of muffins and took them
over to the new neighbor's place to say hi. They
have the coolest tiny home in their back yard.
oh and it turns out their cat's name is Muffin.

THE ANTIDOTE TO FEAR
GRATITUDE

Fear is why we don't take action on our brave intentions and anger is why we get stuck. Choosing to be grateful, however, even if only for a few moments, will transform our perspective from fear and anger to appreciation and contentment.

*Gratitude is the foundation
for which all other intentions are built.*

As we focus on developing bravery, it is imperative that we balance this "desire to become" with an appreciation for the abundance that we already have. By appreciating the positives (big and small) that bring smiles to our faces, we naturally attract more of this same abundance. **That is why there is space each day for gratitude.**

*When the going gets tough,
the tough give thanks.*

By following a courageous act with a moment of gratitude, we increasingly develop the resilience to respond bravely in the face of fear.

Questions to inspire gratitude:

What have others done that I have benefited from?
What have I done that has helped others?
What makes me smile as I take in my surroundings?
What opportunities do I have that I am thankful for?
What have I been given that I didn't earn?

A PLACE FOR NEGATIVITY

BURN PAGES

A place to detach and let
go of untrue thoughts
that are not serving you.

located in the back (pg. 140)

Digging up the weeds.

As we dive inward, there will no doubt be negative thoughts and emotions that surface. There is great value in understanding where those thoughts came from and why they keep nagging us. They are there for a reason. What are they trying to say?

If left untreated, these limiting beliefs and destructive thoughts can begin to take root and pollute the healthy habits we're building.

That's why the 'burn pages' exist.

Any time an unnerving thought arises while journaling, use these 'burn pages' to capture, analyze, and properly let go of negative thoughts.

There is one 'burn page' for each of your 30 days throughout this journal. So each day, when you notice a negative, irritating thought arise, you have a place to put it so you can carry on getting in touch with your innately good, positive, and brave self.

Go ahead and take a look in the back of this journal.

EXPLORING FURTHER

BEYOND THE JOURNAL

A growing collection of Intention Inspired resources and tools are available to you online. Connect with the community, share your experience, and encourage others who have embarked on their own brave adventure.

There is also a free digital companion to this 30-Day Brave Journal that delivers your daily journal prompts and challenges right to your email inbox.

Available at **intentioninspired.com/brave**

"It is good to have an end to journey toward, but it is the journey that matters in the end."

— ERNEST HEMINGWAY

Ready to get started?

Here we stand at the trailhead of change.

To challenge ourselves, to face our fears.

Tiptoeing the boundary of comfort,

with an inspired impulse

to take a leap and spread our wings.

The destination is irrelevant

because the journey is why we're here.

To know more, to feel more, to be more.

Now is the PERFECT TIME for a deep, JUICY BREATH.

Let the adventure begin!

With pure
intention
comes
effortless
action.

WEEK 1

CLARITY
OF INTENT

These initial seven days of our brave adventure begin with an inner journey. By gaining clarity of our intent, we create a solid foundation that empowers brave actions to be implemented when it matters most.

A better understanding of oneself and one's deepest intention gives invaluable insight and direction to charge forward.

Take another deep, delicious breath and know this is the beginning of positive, powerful change.

I AM

Inspired

I am inspired because I can feel a flame inside me pulling me to create more and live life more fully. In any given moment I have the choice to push through resistance, be brave, and fuel that inspiration into courageous action.

What inspired me to start this journal?

_____

_____

☐ *Today, I will choose an object to serve as a reminder of this inspiration:*

make a cairn	plant a seed	wear something	light a candle	use a thingy
a mound of stones	*and grow with it*	*like a mala necklace*	*burn with intent*	*it can be anything*

Embed intention to this object and strategically place/use it with your journal.

What else has inspired me lately?

_____

_____

Common attributes of things that inspire me ...

_____

_____

"From a tiny spark may burst a mighty flame."

— DANTE

I am grateful for ...

_____

_____

_____

Morning inspiration ...

_____

_____

_____

_____

_____

Evening reflection ...

_____

_____

_____

_____

_____

I AM

Committed

I am committed to spending time journaling each day because I know it takes discipline and repetition to truly transform. Some days will be harder than others, but I have the self-discipline to stay the course. This small win will perpetuate more small wins throughout the day making it easier to develop habits that empower brave living.

Committing to this 30-day journal is important to me because ...

_____

_____

_____

☐ *Today, I will hold myself accountable in the following ways:*

Adapt my morning routine:

Invite these buddies to join me:

_____

_____

_____

_____

Public statement of my plan:

Set the following stakes if I fail:

_____

_____

_____

_____

"Commitment means staying loyal to what you said you were
going to do long after the mood you said it in has left you."

– UNKNOWN

I am grateful for ...

_____

_____

_____

Morning inspiration ...

_____

_____

_____

_____

_____

Evening reflection ...

_____

_____

_____

_____

_____

I AM

Self-Aware

I am self-aware because my capacity to confidently charge forward relies solely on my ability to know who I am, and who I want to be. Through self-awareness, I will leverage my strengths and accept my weaknesses. This deeper understanding helps me mindfully manage emotional reactions and skillfully navigate challenging situations.

One of my greatest strengths has always been ...

_____

_____

One of my greatest weaknesses that I acknowledge ...

_____

_____

☐ *Today, I will ask a friend for constructive feedback.*

I know there are blind spots in my thinking patterns and behaviors. So I will openly ask someone who understands me; whom I respect; and will tell me what I need to hear, not what I want to hear. I will cherish honest, outside perspectives because they show me invaluable insight into who I am.

Common outside perspectives of my strengths and weaknesses:

_____

_____

"What is necessary to change a person is to change his awareness of himself."

— ABRAHAM MASLOW

I am grateful for ...

_____

_____

_____

Morning inspiration ...

_____

_____

_____

_____

_____

Evening reflection ...

_____

_____

_____

_____

_____

A doodle of things that come to

mind when I ask myself,

"Who am I?"

I AM

know yourself to
own yourself

I AM

Present

I am present because only *this moment* holds the opportunity for powerful life-changing action. I will not allow my past fears and failures to limit the potential of who I could become today. As I live today moment by moment, I free myself from any stressors of the past and anxiety for the future.

A past moment that left me feeling powerless or afraid ...

_____

_____

_____

If a similar moment were to occur, I have the understanding to navigate through it more courageously by responding in the following way ...

_____

_____

_____

☐ *Today, I will take a moment to count five slow breaths in a row.*

It's not always easy to be present. Flip to the next page to find a guide.

"There is only one time that is important – NOW! It is the most important time because it is the only time that we have any power."

– LEO TOLSTOY

I am grateful for ...

_____

_____

_____

Morning inspiration ...

_____

_____

_____

_____

_____

Evening reflection ...

_____

_____

_____

_____

_____

THE ONE-MINUTE MEDITATION

—//—

Take a deep breath ...

Breathing in through the nose,
Breathing out through the mouth.

Breathing in feeling the lungs expanding,
Breathing out feeling a sense of letting go.

Breathing in to feel the body getting fuller.
Breathing out to feel the release of any tension.

Breathing in feeling more alive and awake.
Breathing out feeling muscles relaxing.

Breathing in that sense of fullness.
Breathing out that unnecessary tension in the body & mind.

Meditation nourishes the mind, like food nourishes the Body.

I AM

Enough

___ / ___ / ___

I am enough as I am willing to let go of who I think I should be, in order be more of who I am. As I journey forward through life's ups and downs I will embrace and appreciate who I have become. I will share the story of who I am, with my whole heart, by letting my truest self be deeply seen. I am worthy of love and belonging because just as I am, right this very moment, I am enough.

How I define feeling 'enough' as it relates to me personally?

_____

_____

☐ *Today, I will spend time listening to my thoughts of 'not enough'.*

Use a 'burn page' (pg. 140) to unload all the ways you've been telling yourself you are not enough. Then rip it out, thank those thoughts for helping you better understand yourself, and let them go as you say, "I am enough."

What are my voices of 'not enough' trying to tell me?

_____

_____

What can these voices teach me?

_____

_____

"You are enough, just as you are. Each emotion you feel, everything you do in your life, everything you do or do not do... where you are and who you are right now is enough. It is perfect. You are perfect enough."

— MELANIE JADE

I am grateful for ...

_____

_____

_____

Morning inspiration ...

_____

_____

_____

_____

_____

_____

Evening reflection ...

_____

_____

_____

_____

_____

_____

I AM

Prepared

I am prepared to connect deeper with myself. By having a greater awareness of my life I establish clarity on my brave intentions. These intentions provide me with a compass toward the experiences I wish to have. Knowing what I want and creating a clear vision will help keep me oriented on my journey toward a braver, bolder life and allow exciting changes to follow.

A clear, concise recommitment of *my 30-day goal:*

_____

Which means within two weeks, I need to *(insert 2-week goal):*

_____

Which means in one week, I need to *(insert 1-week goal):*

_____

Which means in the next three days, I need to *(insert 3-day goal):*

_____

Which means today, I need to *(insert today's goal):*

_____

☐ **Today, I will use the following metric to measure the results of my goal** *(e.g., a daily photo update, progress report, journal log):*

_____

Measuring progress will help me stay on track, reach my target dates, and experience achievement that will propel me to bravely charge forth in the face of fear.

"If you don't know where you are going, you might not get there."

– YOGI BERRA

I am grateful for ...

_____

_____

_____

Morning inspiration ...

_____

_____

_____

_____

_____

Evening reflection ...

_____

_____

_____

_____

_____

Whoa, an empty page? I wasn't *prepared* for that.

Such is life. I will turn this unexpected event into an opportunity by bravely spilling my thoughts, scribbling my mind, and dripping my coffee.

Don't hold back. Let it flow!

I AM

Heroic

I am heroic because forging my own destiny is what springs me out of bed and gives me courage to take brave leaps of faith. Ultimately, only I get to decide how my story unfolds. The stories I tell myself are either limiting or expanding my potential. Today, and every day, I will take an active role in the lifelong adventure of becoming the hero of my own story.

If my life was a movie, what would the hero do?

_____

_____

What old routines and patterns would the hero break?

_____

_____

What new habits would the hero replace those old habits with?

_____

_____

☐ *Today, I will take my favorite powerstance, own it, and declare,*

"I am the hero of my own story!"

"If you are not the hero of your own story,
then you're missing the whole point of your humanity."

– STEVE MARABOLI

I am grateful for ...

_____

_____

_____

Morning inspiration ...

_____

_____

_____

_____

_____

Evening reflection ...

_____

_____

_____

_____

_____

_____

ONE & DONE

—//—

Nice job! This marks a full week of getting in touch with your braver side. As you may have found, it has always been there; eagerly waiting to help you get where you want to go.

—

Reflect on this past week and note how you have gained clarity on your braver intention and why this is important to you.

_____

_____

_____

_____

_____

_____

CONSIDER THAT

A SEED PLANTED

Missed a day or so?

Starting to lose that initial inspiration and drive to take action? Good, that means you're human. What's essential is that we don't beat ourselves up. We can't have the highs without the lows.

Our response to these shortcomings is where the good stuff is! We always have the choice. We can call it in and throw in the towel, or take a moment to catch our breath, get back up, and press on to toward our braver self.

Stay Patient
and trust your
Journey

EVERYBODY'S
—brave is—
DIFFERENT.

WEEK 2

FOUNDATION FOR CHANGE

Just as each seed needs more or less water, a varying degree of sunshine, and perhaps a preferred morning melody, so too does each brave endeavor require its own quality of attention and nourishment. What makes you, me, him, and her blossom into the fullness of our greatest potential will always be different.

By taking what we've learned about our inward dive, we can begin to extrapolate what's needed for our own brave journey and let our seeds take root toward long-term sustainable change.

Get ready, you might surprise yourself »

| I AM |

Capable

I am capable because I have the patience and fortitude to nurture dreams, into goals, into actions, into reality. The feats I've set out to tackle, big and small, are becoming increasingly achievable through my consistent hard work. I will be patient with myself, to let the seeds of my actions take root and grow into something amazing. Through time and effort, I have an expanding capacity to be brave.

Who made you feel good this week? What did they say?

_____

_____

_____

Who taught you something about yourself, humanity, or the world that you at first did not think you wanted to know?

_____

_____

_____

☐ **Today, I will water someone else's seed of brave intention.**

Bring a friend to mind who is uniquely gifted and capable of more.
Send them a word of encouragement to let them know what you see in them.

How did they respond? »

"You must give everything to make your life as beautiful
as the dreams that dance in your imagination."

– ROMAN PAYNE

I am grateful for ...

_____

_____

_____

Morning inspiration ...

_____

_____

_____

_____

_____

Evening reflection ...

_____

_____

_____

_____

_____

_____

I AM

Vulnerable

I am vulnerable because although my insecurities are at the core of what I fear, these vulnerabilities are the birthplace of my joy, creativity, and love. So I will compassionately embrace my imperfections because feeling so fiercely vulnerable means I am alive. I will let myself be deeply seen and share myself wholeheartedly even though there are no guarantees that things will work out.

When have I been afraid of being rejected?

_____

_____

How has the fear of rejection been limiting me?

_____

_____

A weakness that I'm struggling with ...

_____

_____

☐ **Today, I will be courageously vulnerable by sharing this weakness with the following person:**

_____   *How did it go?* »

"To share your weakness is to make yourself vulnerable;
to make yourself vulnerable is to show your strength."

— CRISS JAMI

I am grateful for ...

_____

_____

_____

Morning inspiration ...

_____

_____

_____

_____

_____

_____

Evening reflection ...

_____

_____

_____

_____

_____

_____

I AM

____ / ____ / ____

Curious

I am curious because to know the truth I have to be willing to look. Each time I let go of the need to be right and stay in that vulnerable place of uncertainty, I embrace the kind of curiosity that develops awareness and discovery. When faced with fear, my curiosity asks, 'Why am I scared of this fear?' Responding to fear with interrogation creates space for courageous action.

A recent fear that I would like to overcome ...

_____

Why does this fear make me feel scared and uncomfortable?

_____

Why does it matter to me that I overcome this fear?

_____

Why have I previously been unable to overcome this fear?

_____

☐ **Today, I will ask three consecutive 'whys' to someone today.**

How did this inspire deeper dialogue? »

*"You can never cross the ocean unless you
have the courage to lose sight of the shore."*

— ANDRE GIDE

I am grateful for ...

_____

_____

_____

Morning inspiration ...

_____

_____

_____

_____

_____

Evening reflection ...

_____

_____

_____

_____

_____

_____

I AM

Compassionate

I am compassionate because my fears become my ally when I look to them with a genuine curiosity for what they're trying to say. Every fear I experience is a part of me that has grown out of the experiences I've had. By acknowledging these fears, and listening to them, I can begin to understand why they're there ... most often they're just trying to keep me safe, and usually, I can just let them know that I'm already safe. I can let the insistent voice of fear fade away because I am compassionate.

A recent situation that is creating anxiety and/or stress ...

_____

_____

How can I embrace this fear with compassion and kindness?

_____

_____

☐ **Today, I will try to recognize a moment of discomfort and instead of ignoring or disregarding it, I will really try to feel it, listen to, and love it for being there.**

Use the short exercise on the following page.

"Compassion is the courage to descend into the reality of human experience."

— PAUL GILBERT

I am grateful for ...

_____

_____

_____

Morning inspiration ...

_____

_____

_____

_____

_____

Evening reflection ...

_____

_____

_____

_____

_____

A current situation that is causing me stress:

_____

_____

_____

•

As this situation comes to mind feel the stress
and emotional discomfort in your body.

•

Now, speak into that feeling of discomfort:

*"This is a moment of suffering. Suffering
is a part of life. I will treat this suffering
with compassion and kindness."*

•

Use a burn page in back of this journal to explore
this stress deeper and further grow from it.

COMPASSION
without →
ACTION (is)
OBSERVATION

I AM

___ / ___ / ___

Calculated

I am calculated because the more diligent I am in calculating each risky decision, the more prepared I am to prevent the worst from happening. In turn, I have more clarity and confidence to take that next brave step forward. When fear stops me in my tracks, I will remember that every daunting challenge can be broken down into a series of smaller calculated risks.

Something I know I need to move forward with ...

_____

_____

An unknown that makes me hesitant to proceed ...

_____

_____

One thing I will do today to gain clarity on the path forward ...

_____

_____

☐ **Today, I will say 'no' to a pending invitation or opportunity that would deter me from my 30-day goal.**

What did you get done instead? »

> *"Often the difference between a successful person and a failure is not one's better abilities or ideas, but the courage that one has to bet on his ideas, to take a calculated risk, and to act."*
>
> — MAXWELL MALTZ

I am grateful for ...

_____

_____

_____

Morning inspiration ...

_____

_____

_____

_____

_____

Evening reflection ...

_____

_____

_____

_____

_____

Ambitious

I am ambitious because when I'm acting from a place of ambition, I'm guaranteed at least some form of success. What are the chances that I will get what I want without going after it? Slim to none. I will live up to my potential by taking the initiative to make that brave step toward what I really want.

What might prevent me from acting from my braver self today?

_____

_____

_____

What might be the single biggest barrier preventing me from accomplishing what I've set out to do?

_____

_____

_____

☐ Today, I will mitigate the risk of limiting barriers by defining <u>one simple thing</u> I can do every day, *no matter what*, to make progress toward my 30-Day Goal:

_____

_____

"Start by doing what's necessary; then do what's possible;
and suddenly you are doing the impossible."

— FRANCIS OF ASSISI

I am grateful for ...

_____

_____

_____

Morning inspiration ...

_____

_____

_____

_____

_____

Evening reflection ...

_____

_____

_____

_____

_____

_____

I AM

___ / ___ / ___

Determined

I am determined because I know my lot in life is created by the actions I have and haven't taken. Today, I will do what I know needs to be done to accomplish what I've set out to achieve. I have the will and skill to fight through resistance and understand the fears that I encounter. I will not run from them. I will embrace them and in doing so, overcome them.

What has previously interfered with my ability to act bravely (e.g., limiting beliefs, values, people, systems, etc)?

_____

_____

_____

Why it is important for me to overcome the fears of these conflicts ...

_____

_____

_____

☐ **Today, I will be patient and stay determined with the small, *seemingly* insignificant things.**

"A dream doesn't become reality through magic;
it takes sweat, determination and hard work."

— COLIN POWELL

I am grateful for ...

_____

_____

_____

Morning inspiration ...

_____

_____

_____

_____

_____

Evening reflection ...

_____

_____

_____

_____

_____

_____

I am determined to write, "I am determined"
ten times with my opposite hand:

1. _____

2. _____

3. _____

4. _____

5. _____

6. _____

7. _____

8. _____

9. _____

10. _____

Progress
takes place
outside the
COMFORT
ZONE.

H A L F W A Y   T H E R E !

Quality work! Perhaps you're starting to surprise yourself as you realize how brave you already are. Often all it takes to make a radical shift toward self-confidence and brave action is overcoming a single barrier or just a realization from getting to know yourself better.

—

Reflect on the past two weeks and note what you have learned about yourself that has allowed you to naturally act more brave.

_____

_____

_____

_____

_____

CONSIDER THAT

A SEED WATERED

Feeling exhausted?

Remember WHY you set out on this particular journey in the first place. Try it now: really feel why this intention is so important to you. Let your 'why' re-spark your enthusiasm and pull you into action. When our why is clear and our actions align, we can stop pushing and let that inspiring energy propel us after what matters most.

As journaling becomes more ingrained in the everyday routine, among other self-development practices, it is essential that the intentions driving us are true and honest to what YOU want, not what anyone else wants.

Never forget your why.

Don't predict
the future,
create it.

H A B I T S

& R O U T I N E S

As we continue to put in the time to intentionally flex that brave muscle, we are gradually adopting more fearless normals. But being brave isn't just about what we do, it's also about what we believe. By redefining how courage applies to oneself and reconsidering what's possible, we can aptly put our goals within reach, at our own pace, on our own terms. By clearly grasping what's possible, any doubt of what we're capable of starts to fade.

For the next seven days, we will find ways to adjust our habits and routines that will foster long-term courageous action toward a more active, fulfilling life.

Warning: others might ask, "What happened to you lately?" »

I AM

Resourceful

I am resourceful in recognizing the needs, beliefs, and emotions that are controlling me so I can develop further confidence in my journey forward. My ability to appreciate and contribute does not depend on my access to resources. The fact that I'm using this journal is proof that I have recognized a need in myself and had the resourcefulness to acquire tools to help take me where I want to go.

What resources would help me flourish in my brave endeavors (e.g., money, time, information, training, technology, people)?

_____

_____

_____

What emotions can I develop to elicit more of those resources (e.g., creativity, curiosity, determination, love, enthusiasm, honesty)?

_____

_____

_____

☐ **Today, I will feel what emotions arise as I doodle a photo of myself, 15 days from now, succeeding in achieving my 30-day goal.** There is space for this on the following page (86).

Now is no time to think of what you do not have.
Think of what you can do with what there is.

— ERNEST HEMINGWAY

I am grateful for …

_____

_____

_____

Morning inspiration …

_____

_____

_____

_____

_____

Evening reflection …

_____

_____

_____

_____

_____

A scene of my future self.

Where do I live? Who am I with? What do I have?

A log of emotions that arise as I doodle:

_____

_____

_____

_____

_____

_____

Power over emotions,
is power to shape
DESTINY.

I AM

Focused

_____ / _____ / _____

I am focused because when I decide to give something my undivided attention, powerful emotions are created that inspire brave action. What's great is I always have complete control on where and how I direct my focus. Having a clear desired outcome and consistently focusing on it immediately changes my behavior, giving me the momentum I need to take daily actions that will lead to profound results.

Something I recently achieved that I might have previously thought impossible …

_____

_____

_____

Someone or something that will get 100% of my attention today:

_____

_____

_____

☐ **Today, I will pay extra attention to simple every day tasks.** Feel the shower, taste the toothpaste, and hear the birds sing.

"The secret of change is to focus all of your energy,
not on fighting the old, but on building the new."

— SOCRATES

I am grateful for ...

_____

_____

_____

Morning inspiration ...

_____

_____

_____

_____

_____

Evening reflection ...

_____

_____

_____

_____

_____

_____

I AM

Progressing

I am progressing even though sometimes when I take one step forward, it feels like I end up falling two steps back. I know that as I continue on my journey it is essential that I don't let these setbacks deter me from staying the course and moving forward. I must remember that life moves in waves and it's okay to have bad days, as long as I get back up and keep pressing ahead.

A recent moment that left me feeling scared and discouraged …

_____

_____

_____

By reflecting on this moment, I see now that I grew from this challenging situation in the following way …

_____

_____

_____

☐ **Today, I will let my brave muscle repair and strengthen by reflecting and appreciating the daily small wins I've been accomplishing.**

"Develop resilience and be brave. There are days when it is very discouraging. You have to develop personal resilience to environmental things that come along. If you let every single environmental challenge knock you off your game, it's going to be very, very hard."

— RENEE JAMES

I am grateful for ...

Morning inspiration ...

Evening reflection ...

A few of my favorite small wins along this journey ...

BIG WINS
are just a bunch of small
WINS.

I AM

Adventurous

I am adventurous because it is through direct experience that I develop a concrete understanding of my own reality. This develops self confidence at a cellular level that enables me to freely and courageously navigate any adventure. I know I might not find the answer or reach the destination I set out for, but this quest of inquiry will at least open myself up to a mystery that's meant to be lived.

What assumed truth is preventing me from taking action?

_____

_____

_____

What personal experience could give me a better understanding of this fear?

_____

_____

_____

☐ **Today, I will adventurously ask a stranger the first genuine question that comes to mind.**

"Nothing in life is to be feared, it is only to be understood.
Now is the time to understand more, so that we may fear less."

— MARIE CURIE

I am grateful for ...

_____

_____

_____

Morning inspiration ...

_____

_____

_____

_____

_____

Evening reflection ...

_____

_____

_____

_____

_____

_____

I AM

Optimistic

I am optimistic because navigating difficulty in this positive light turns obstacles into opportunities and empowers me to press on courageously. As I encounter fear and opposition, I will greet it with an extra degree of kindness and care. I will let the curve of my smile grow into every negative thought and emotion.

When things inevitably don't go my way today, I will use optimism to overcome adversity by responding in the following way ...

_____

_____

_____

How I've seen positive reinforcement work to help change my behavior ...

_____

_____

_____

☐ **Today, in a moment of misery, crack a smile.**
To prep yourself for this moment, try to force a giggle (maybe even a full-on belly laugh) right now.

"Every day is a new beginning. Treat it that way.
Stay away from what might have been and look at what can be."

— MARSHA PETRIE SUE

I am grateful for ...

_____

_____

_____

Morning inspiration ...

_____

_____

_____

_____

_____

_____

Evening reflection ...

_____

_____

_____

_____

_____

_____

I AM

Outgoing

___ / ___ / ___

I am outgoing because memories and goals are much more satisfying when savored with others. From best friends to complete strangers, I listen sincerely because each perspective brings its own unique value. An attitude of understanding removes barriers and allows for mutual constructive growth. I always seek to recognize the potential in others and will encourage them in their own brave intentions.

What conversation do I need to have that I've been putting off?

_____

_____

_____

What am I scared of that has prevented me from having this conversation?

_____

_____

_____

☐ **Today, I will commit to one uncomfortable conversation.**

How did it go? »

"And by the way, everything in life is writable about if you have the outgoing guts to do it, and the imagination to improvise. The worst enemy to creativity is self-doubt."

– SYLVIA PLATH

I am grateful for ...

_____

_____

_____

Morning inspiration ...

_____

_____

_____

_____

_____

_____

Evening reflection ...

_____

_____

_____

_____

_____

_____

I AM

Humble

I am humble because taking that brave step forward may be scary, but it doesn't have to be a mystery. Someone has already climbed the mountain I am climbing and taken the steps I want to take. More often than not, these mentors would be honored to share how they did it and what they would've done differently. I will be brave by not being scared or ashamed to ask for help.

How has humility provided a useful perspective on my life and how it should be lived?

_____

_____

_____

I would like more guidance in the following area ...

_____

_____

_____

☐ **Today, I will reach out to the following person to ask for help with this ...** _____

What did they say and how did they help? »

"We should be inspired by people... who show that human beings can be kind, brave, generous, beautiful, strong-even in the most difficult circumstances."

— RACHEL CORRIE

I am grateful for ...

_____

_____

_____

Morning inspiration ...

_____

_____

_____

_____

_____

_____

Evening reflection ...

_____

_____

_____

_____

_____

_____

HOME STRETCH!

—//—

You're crushing it! Have you noticed how this inner journey reflects on the outer world? Every thought, decision, and action we take toward owning our braver intentions have a massive rippling impact on our environment and every person we come in contact with.

—

Reflect on ways you have prioritized your internal needs and note how the external things are beginning to change in your favor as a result:

_____

_____

_____

_____

_____

_____

CONSIDER THAT

A SEED SPROUTED

Whew, wee!

Nobody said it was going to be easy, but we did say it was going to be worth it. It is those moments when resistance is at its peak, and we feel like we're getting dragged through the mud that we have the opportunity to get in touch with our imperfect self. It is during these times, during our lowest of lows, that we have the best chance to understand what kind of self-work is needed to rise with resilience.

HoLD tHe VISION. TRUSt THE PROCESS.

LUCK FAVORS
the prepared

From a tiny Seed grew @ Mighty tree

WEEK 4

EMBODY THE BRAVE

—#—

With a greater clarity of intent, a solid foundation to build from, and habits and routines that are guiding our actions, we're fully primed to embody our inherently braver self.

You've likely found the tools and tactics we've been focusing on over the past few weeks can be implemented anywhere. Every situation holds it's own opportunity to apply what we've discovered, to challenge our limiting beliefs, to fail courageously, and to blossom bravely toward our most heartfelt aspirations.

The daily focus for these last seven days lives at the heart of what it means to be brave. To unleash our inner lion and let out a relentless roar in the face of fear.

It's time to own who you were born to be »

I AM

Grateful

I am grateful because, if only for a few moments, gratitude transforms my perspective of fear and anger to appreciation and contentment. Fear is why I don't take action on my intentions and anger is why I get stuck. I remind myself that it is impossible to be fearful while being grateful at the same time. Gratitude then, is my ultimate go-to tool for navigating bravely through the journey ahead.

Something I can see in my environment that brings me joy ...

_____

_____

A recent coincidence that left me with a smile ...

_____

_____

A person I am blessed to have in my life right now ...

_____

_____

☐ **Today, set 3 gratitude alarms to go off at random times during today.** As they alarm, stop whatever it is your doing and bring to mind 3 things you're grateful for in that moment. ☺

"When you are grateful fear disappears and abundance appears."

— TONY ROBBINS

I am *extra* grateful today for ...

_____

_____

_____

Morning inspiration ...

_____

_____

_____

_____

_____

Evening reflection ...

_____

_____

_____

_____

_____

_____

I AM

Risky

I am risky because my life is colored by the risks I take. I will never regret taking action because it's what has molded me into who I have become. Failure is a result. Rejection is a result. So when I go for it and fail, I at least have something to learn from. It's the things I don't do that eat away me because of the unknown of what could have happened ... If I never try, I will never know.

An area in my life I need to take more calculated risks ...

_____

_____

_____

How does *not* taking action toward my 30-day goal affect me and the people I care about?

_____

_____

_____

☐ **Today, I will approach someone who intimidates me and give them a compliment.**

How did they respond? »

"Take chances, make mistakes. That's how you grow. Pain nourishes your courage. You have to fail in order to practice being brave."

— MARY TYLER MOORE

I am grateful for ...

Morning inspiration ...

Evening reflection ...

I AM

Persistent

I am persistent in facing with my fears because I embrace why it is important to face them in the first place. Holding that vision in mind fuels me to act boldly and press on. I don't always get far, but that doesn't really matter. What does matters is that I don't turn around because fighting through the hard times is when I grow the most. I will put in the work and hit it with all I've got.

A restatement of my 30-Day Goal and *why* it's important ...

_____

_____

A recent moment I felt like giving up, but didn't ...

_____

_____

What is it that pulls me forward despite the urge to quit?

_____

_____

☐ **Today, I will commit to 3 persistent asks in a row.**
Next time I get a 'no', I will ask again. And again. Then ask at least one more time.

"Anyone who has a why to live can bear almost any what."

— NIETZSCHE

I am grateful for ...

_____

_____

_____

Morning inspiration ...

_____

_____

_____

_____

_____

_____

Evening reflection ...

_____

_____

_____

_____

_____

_____

I AM

Resilient

I am resilient because no matter how much I plan and prepare I can't always dodge the setbacks of life's uncertainties. What's important is when life gets me up against the rope, I will not give up, I will not give in. If it were easy, everyone would be doing it. I will stand my ground and remember why I set out on this brave adventure in the first place. I will take a breath, look forward, and say "Bring it on."

What is the cost if I don't take action on my 30-Day Goal?

_____

_____

_____

How does weighing the costs of inaction create a spark to take necessary action?

_____

_____

_____

☐ **Today, I will get the following done, *no matter what*:**

_____

"All you gotta do is outlast."

– BUSTER DOUGLAS'S MOM

Buster Douglas was the first boxer to knock out Mike Tyson,

after getting knocked out himself in the previous round.

I am grateful for ...

_____

_____

_____

Morning inspiration ...

_____

_____

_____

_____

_____

Evening reflection ...

_____

_____

_____

_____

_____

EuStress

I am eustress as I grin amidst any discomfort knowing that this healthy stress is what makes my brave muscles stretch and grow. In order to get something I don't have, or go somewhere I've never been, I have to do something I've never done. This is why I'm willing to step outside my comfort zone and do things that make me feel uncomfortable. As I condition myself to master my fear of discomfort in small doses, I notice my comfort zone slowly expand to include discomfort.

What type of stress has made me stronger along this journey?

_____

_____

_____

How can I invite more healthy stress into my life to replace unhealthy stress?

_____

_____

_____

☐ **Today, I will condition myself to be more okay with discomfort by intentionally doing the following ...**

_____

Keep it simple and goofy like wear mismatched socks or wear your shirt inside out.

"Discomfort is very much part of my master plan."

— JONATHAN LETHEM

I am grateful for …

_____

_____

_____

Morning inspiration …

_____

_____

_____

_____

_____

Evening reflection …

_____

_____

_____

_____

_____

_____

I AM

Confident

I am confident with my body and mind. To think confidently, I must move confidently because motions are the precursor to emotions. Which is why it's often easier to act my way into a new line of thinking than to think my way into a new line of acting. I avoid actions that elicit guilt, because guilt will eat at my self-confidence. Taking constructive action on what I feel is right will keep my conscience satisfied and build up self-confidence.

When do I feel genuinely confident?

_____

_____

_____

What can I do today to *act* my way into more self-confidence *(e.g., make more eye contact, start the conversation, walk taller and faster)*?

_____

_____

_____

☐ **Today, I will answer every question that is asked of me with a confident 'YES' or 'NO'.**

"Confidence is like a muscle: the more you use it, the stronger it gets."

— UNKNOWN

I am grateful for …

_____

_____

_____

Morning inspiration …

_____

_____

_____

_____

_____

Evening reflection …

_____

_____

_____

_____

_____

_____

I AM

Changing

I am changing because life is always changing. Remembering this gives me comfort and confidence for whatever the day may hold. I drift smoothly through those changes, good and bad. When things get stormy, I take comfort knowing this too shall pass and any current pain will subside. When good things drift away from me, I take comfort knowing better things await on the journey ahead.

Reflecting back a month, I have changed in the following way ...

_____

_____

_____

Looking a month ahead, I expect to change in the following way ...

_____

_____

_____

☐ **Today, I will ask someone who knows me well,**

   "What is the biggest change you have noticed most in me lately?"

How did they respond? »

"Change can be beautiful when we are brave enough to evolve with it, and change can be brutal when we fearfully resist."

— BRYANT MCGILL

I am grateful for ...

Morning inspiration ...

Evening reflection ...

Growing

I am growing as I feel the power of consistent micro acts of bravery. It's fulfilling because it's growing into something far beyond my small self. So I will continue to live life in ever widening circles, trying to make each ripple further than the last.

What do I notice compounding into something greater that would have been impossible for me to see a month ago?

_____

_____

_____

What might happen if I stayed committed toward this growth for another 30 days?

_____

_____

_____

☐ **Reach out to a friend whom you've lost touch. Ask them how they've grown and try to pinpoint what the real driving force for their action to change was.**

What did you learn? »

"Change can be beautiful when we are brave enough to evolve with it, and change can be brutal when we fearfully resist."

– BRYANT MCGILL

I am grateful for ...

_____

_____

_____

Morning inspiration ...

_____

_____

_____

_____

_____

Evening reflection ...

_____

_____

_____

_____

_____

I am brave because I put in the time to strengthen my brave muscle. I challenged myself, I took action, I stepped out of my comfort zone, I took risks, I felt vulnerable, and I accomplished what I set out to do. It is not easy facing fears, and the journey will never truly be over, but I have built a solid foundation and will continue putting in the hard work because *I am brave*.

What was the most insightful thing you learned about yourself in the past 30 days?

_____

_____

_____

What is one thing that you are going to incorporate into your daily routine to help you live a brave, bold life?

_____

_____

_____

☐ **Today, reward yourself with something nice.
Really nice. You've earned it.**

"Don't be afraid of your fears. They're not there to scare you. They're there to let you know that something is worth it."

— C. JOYBELL C

I am grateful for ...

Morning inspiration ...

Evening reflection ...

B R A V O !

What an adventure.

This is truly a milestone to be cherished. You showed up, put in the self-work, and came out a stronger, braver you! As you know by now, the journey is not always easy, but well worth the work.

We are overwhelmed with gratitude.

We want to thank you and congratulate you for choosing this journal and having committed to the journey. We put together a little congratulations gift for completing this 30 Days of Brave Journal.

Please visit **intentioninspired.com/complete** to share your experience and claim your gift!

CONSIDER THAT

A SEED BLOSSOMED

THE TAKEAWAYS

You have now equipped yourself with 30 days of quality self-work! It's well worth taking a moment to look back to reflect on this incredible journey.

Spend some quality time revisiting each day. Relish the memories. Re-experience the highs and lows. Recognize how you've grown and blossomed into your braver, more confident self.

A reflection on my brave 30-day adventure:

In what way did I surprise myself?

_____

_____

_____

A favorite moment worth cherishing ...

_____

_____

_____

One of the most challenging aspects of this journey ...

_____

_____

_____

How do I know myself better now?

How will I now live more true to my authentic self?

What I will do to leverage the momentum of this change ...

Someone I know that could benefit from this ...

Other key takeaways I've derived from this experience ...

_____

_____

_____

_____

_____

_____

_____

_____

_____

_____

_____

_____

_____

_____

_____

_____

_____

_____

THE NEXT ADVENTURE

W H A T   N O W ?

Just as you are devoted to a life of growth and self-improvement, we are dedicated to creating ongoing tools and services to inspire and equip you to continue your journey. Choose from a variety of products and services designed and developed with loving intent at **intentioninspired.com**

Have an idea or feedback? We always look to our thriving like-minded community first to develop our offerings and inspire our next creation.

Feel free to reach out any time to
hi@intentioninspired.com

and the = =journey goes on

LET IT GO

BURN PAGES

These next 30 pages are yours to unload negative, fear ridden thoughts. To release the weight off your heart and mind with a curious interest of understanding. Go ahead and jot them down, question them, learn from them, and burn them away with intent.

When it hurts, Observe.

INHALE POSITIVITY

RELEASE THE TENSION

EXPERIENCE THE PEACE

IN WITH THE NEW

PLANT NEW SEEDS

THE BLUE SKY IS FOUND

REFOCUS THE LENS

TOUCH WITHOUT HINDER

RELEARN

PULL

FLOW

I AM WHAT I AM

NOTES TO SELF

The End
of ONE Story

is the
beginning
of Another.

Made in the USA
Middletown, DE
18 July 2017